Contents

Introduction

This book has been specifically designed to help you prepare for your GCSE exams in the easiest and most effective way. Keep this book with you throughout your revision – it is the key to your success.

How to use this book

All the information you need to know for your course is presented as a series of brief facts and explanations. these will help you understand and remember your work. You can work through the book chapter by chapter or you can find individual topics by using the index at the back of the book. The example below shows how pages are organised to help you revise each topic.

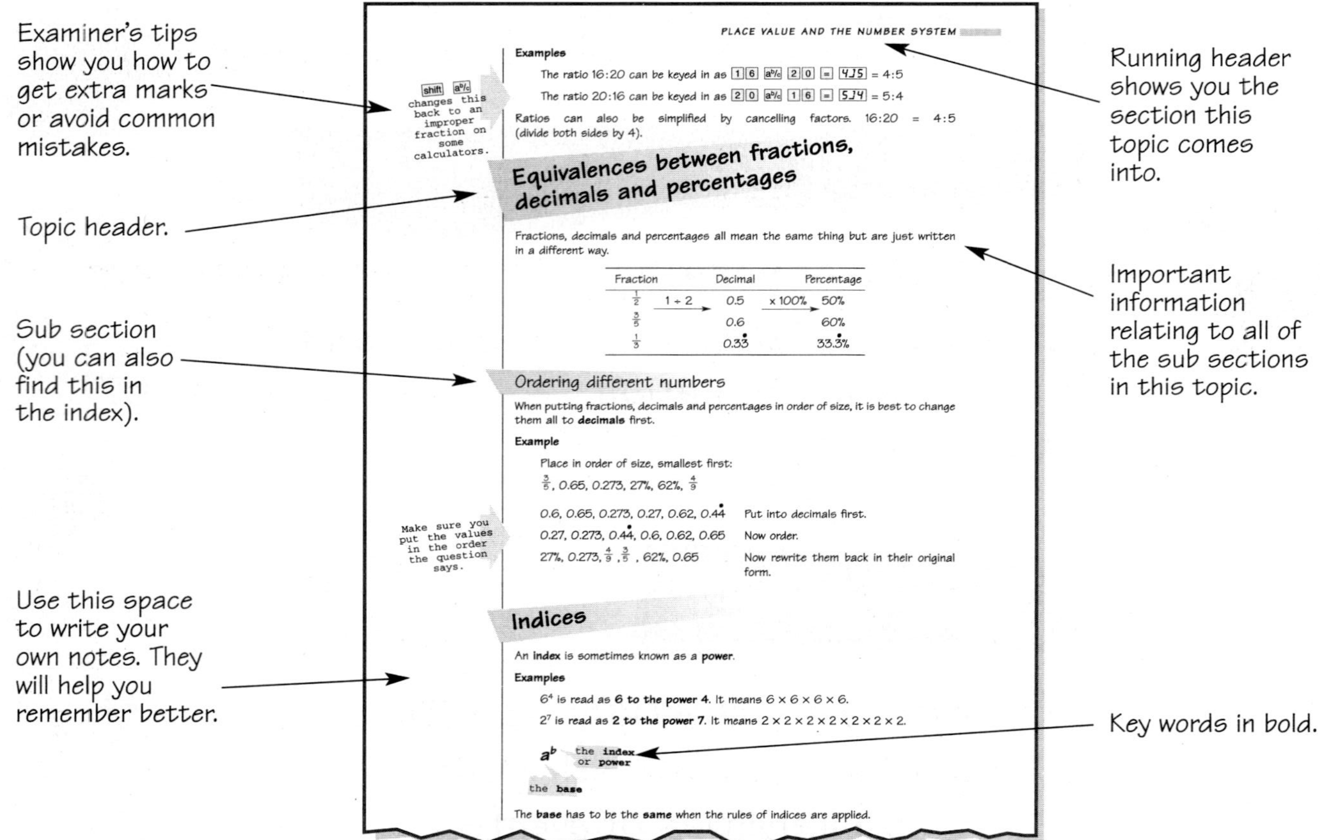

PLACE VALUE AND THE NUMBER SYSTEM

shift a b/c changes this back to an improper fraction on some calculators.

Examples

The ratio 16:20 can be keyed in as 1 6 a b/c 2 0 = 4⌟5 = 4:5

The ratio 20:16 can be keyed in as 2 0 a b/c 1 6 = 5⌟4 = 5:4

Ratios can also be simplified by cancelling factors. 16:20 = 4:5 (divide both sides by 4).

Equivalences between fractions, decimals and percentages

Fractions, decimals and percentages all mean the same thing but are just written in a different way.

Fraction		Decimal		Percentage
$\frac{1}{2}$	1 ÷ 2	0.5	× 100%	50%
$\frac{3}{5}$		0.6		60%
$\frac{1}{3}$		$0.\dot{3}3$		$33.\dot{3}\%$

Ordering different numbers

When putting fractions, decimals and percentages in order of size, it is best to change them all to **decimals** first.

Example

Place in order of size, smallest first:

$\frac{3}{5}$, 0.65, 0.273, 27%, 62%, $\frac{4}{9}$

Make sure you put the values in the order the question says.

0.6, 0.65, 0.273, 0.27, 0.62, $0.\dot{4}4$ — Put into decimals first.

0.27, 0.273, $0.\dot{4}4$, 0.6, 0.62, 0.65 — Now order.

27%, 0.273, $\frac{4}{9}$, $\frac{3}{5}$, 62%, 0.65 — Now rewrite them back in their original form.

Indices

An **index** is sometimes known as a **power**.

Examples

6^4 is read as **6 to the power 4**. It means 6 × 6 × 6 × 6.

2^7 is read as **2 to the power 7**. It means 2 × 2 × 2 × 2 × 2 × 2 × 2.

a^b the **index** or **power**; the **base**

The **base** has to be the **same** when the rules of indices are applied.

Examiner's tips show you how to get extra marks or avoid common mistakes.

Topic header.

Sub section (you can also find this in the index).

Use this space to write your own notes. They will help you remember better.

Running header shows you the section this topic comes into.

Important information relating to all of the sub sections in this topic.

Key words in bold.

Preparing your revision programme

In most subjects you will have coursework, homework, revision, practice examination questions and a final examination. The examination may cause you the most anxiety. With proper preparation, however, you do not need to worry. Remember that there is a short test at the end of each topic. This test will help your understanding and boost your memory. Make sure that you have allowed enough time to revise your work and make a list of all the things you have to do and your coursework deadlines.

Revision Notes

GCSE SUCCESS

Mathematics Intermediate

Author
Fiona C Mapp

Series editor
Alan Brewerton

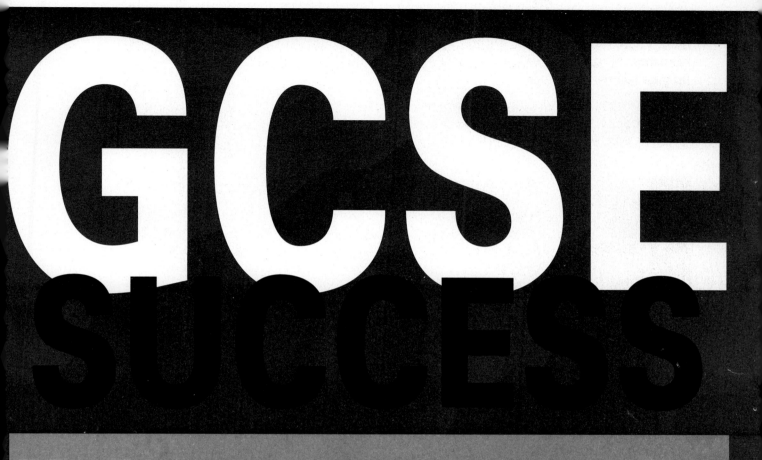

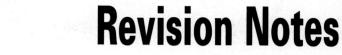

First published 1997
Reprinted 1997, 1998
New edition 1998
This edition 1999

Letts Educational, 9–15 Aldine Street, London W12 8AW
Tel. 0208 740 2270
Fax. 0208 740 2280

Editorial, design and production by Hart McLeod, Cambridge

British Library Cataloguing-in-Publication Data
A CIP record for this book is available from the British Library

ISBN 1 84085 293 3

Printed and bound in Italy

Letts Educational is the trading name of BPP (Letts Educational) Ltd

Acknowledgements
The author and publisher are grateful to the staff at Cottenham Village College, Cambridge, for their technical assistance.

The examiner's report

Every year the examination boards publish reports on the previous year's examinations. The reports show areas in the examinations where students have performed well or badly and highlights mistakes that students frequently make. The examiners' reports can help you avoid making mistakes and therefore gain extra marks. **Recent examiners' reports highlight the following areas where students lost marks.**

- Lack of appropriate equipment, for example protractors, compasses and rulers.
- Insufficient or confused working out. In questions requiring calculations answers were often rounded off too quickly or not given to the required accuracy, e.g. 2 d.p. or 3 s.f., etc.
- Lack of correct units, particularly in questions where you are told to state your units.
- Vague answers with little reference to the data when answering questions which ask you to 'Explain'.
- Lack of knowledge of metric and imperial conversions.
- Inability to use your calculators efficiently, particularly in topics of standard form, substitution of formulae, trigonometry and powers.
- Poor skills in algebraic manipulation, e.g. the ability to solve equations and inequalities.

Common areas of difficulty

Some common areas of difficulty on Intermediate Level examination papers have occurred in the following topics:

- Standard index form *page* 12
- Percentage increase or decrease *page* 21
- Reverse percentage problems *page* 21
- Compound interest *page* 26
- Drawing and interpretation of graphs *pages* 32–36
- Brackets, factorisation and rearranging formulae *pages* 39–41
- Solving simultaneous and quadratic equations *pages* 42–44
- Inequalities *pages* 44–45
- The application of Pythagoras' theorem and trigonometry to problems *page* 53
- Transformations *pages* 58–61
- Similarity *pages* 61–62
- Locus *pages* 64–65
- Dimensions *page* 72
- Averages of grouped data *page* 81
- Using averages to compare distributions *page* 83
- Relative frequency *pages* 86–87
- Tree diagrams *pages* 88–89

Most of all: **Good luck with your revision and your examinations.**

Number and algebra

Place value and the number system

Integers

Examiner's tips and your notes

The integers are the set of numbers {. . ., −3, −2, −1, 0, 1, 2, 3, . . .}.

When referring to integers, the term **integral value** is used. A number that is **non-integral** is not an integer.

Directed numbers

These are numbers which may be **positive** or **negative**. Positive are above zero, negative are below zero.

Negative ← → Positive

−10 −9 −8 −7 −6 −5 −4 −3 −2 −1 0 1 2 3 4 5 6 7 8 9 10

Getting smaller ← → Getting bigger

Examples

−10 is smaller than −8. $-10 < -8$

−4 is bigger than −8. $-4 > -8$

2 is bigger than −6. $2 > -6$

Adding and subtracting directed numbers

Example
The temperature at 6 a.m. was −5 °C. By 10 a.m. it had risen 8 degrees. So the new temperature was 3 °C.

Draw a number line if it helps.

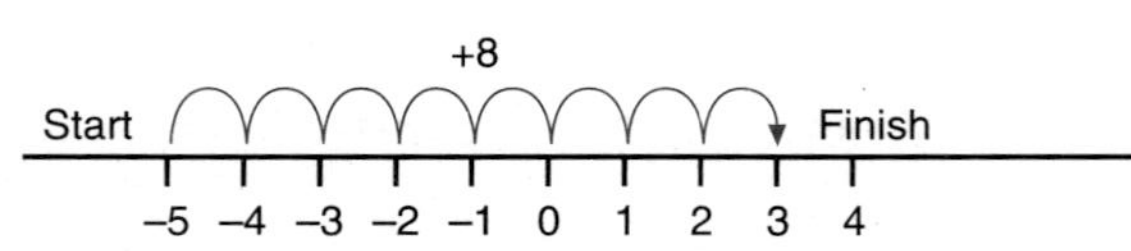

Example
Find the value of −2 − 4.

Note the different uses of the minus sign.

−2 − 4

This represents the **sign** of the number. Start at −2.

This represents the operation of **subtraction**. Move 4 places to the left.

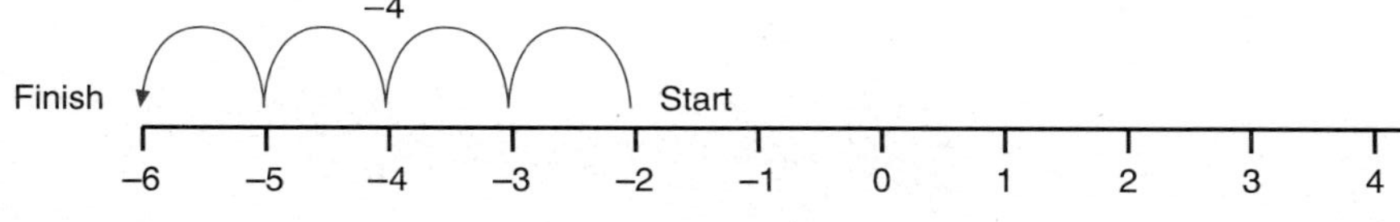

So $-2 - 4 = -6$

When the number to be added (or subtracted) is **negative**, the normal direction of movement is **reversed**.

Example

$-4 - (-3)$ is the same as $-4 + 3 = -1$

The negative changes the direction.

Move 3 places to the right.

When two (+) or two (–) signs are together, these rules are used:

$+(+) \rightarrow +$, $-(-) \rightarrow +$ } **like** signs give a **positive**, $+(-) \rightarrow -$, $-(+) \rightarrow -$ } **unlike** signs give a **negative**.

Examples

$-6 + (-2) = -6 - 2 = -8$ $\quad$ $-2 - (+6) = -2 - 6 = -8$

$4 - (-3) = 4 + 3 = 7$ $\quad$ $9 + (-3) = 9 - 3 = 6$

Multiplying and dividing directed numbers

Multiply and divide the numbers as normal. Then find the sign for the answer using these rules:

- two **like** signs (both + or both –) give **positive**,
- two **unlike** signs (one + and the other –) give **negative**.

Examples

$-6 \times (+4) = -24$ $\quad$ $-12 \div (-3) = 4$

$-6 \times (-3) = 18$ $\quad$ $20 \div (-4) = -5$

Negative numbers on the calculator

Use a calculator when working with negative numbers (if possible).

The [+/–] or [(–)] key on the calculator gives a negative number.

For example, to get –6, press [6] [+/–] or [(–)] [6].

This represents the sign.

Example

$-4 - (-2) = -2$

is keyed in the calculator like this:

[4] [+/–] [–] [2] [+/–] [=]

sign — operation — sign

Make sure you know how to enter it in **your** calculator.

Fractions

A fraction is a part of a whole one. $\frac{4}{5}$ means 4 parts out of 5.

The top number is the **numerator**. The bottom one is the **denominator**.

A fraction like $\frac{4}{5}$ is called a **proper fraction**.

A fraction like $\frac{24}{17}$ is called an **improper fraction**.

Using the fraction key on the calculator

[a b/c] is the fraction key on the calculator.

Example

$\frac{12}{18}$ is keyed in as [1] [2] [a b/c] [1] [8].

This is displayed as [12⌟18] or [12⌐18].

The calculator will automatically cancel down fractions when the [=] key is pressed. For example, $\frac{12}{18}$ becomes [2⌟3] or [2⌐3].

This means two-thirds.

A display of [1⌟4⌟9] means $1\frac{4}{9}$. If you now press [shift] [a b/c], it converts back to an improper fraction, [13⌟9].

Check: your calculator may have a [2nd] or [inv] key instead of [shift].

Decimals

A *decimal* point is used to separate whole-number columns from fractional columns.

Example

Thousands	Hundreds	Tens	Units		Tenths	Hundredths	Thousandths
5	9	2	4	•	1	6	3

decimal point

This number would read as five thousand nine hundred and twenty four point one six three.

- The 1 means $\frac{1}{10}$.
- The 6 means $\frac{6}{100}$.
- The 3 means $\frac{3}{1000}$.

Remember, hundredths are smaller than tenths.
$\frac{10}{100} = \frac{1}{10}$ so $\frac{6}{100} < \frac{1}{10}$

Recurring decimals

A decimal that **recurs** is shown by placing a dot over the numbers that repeat.

Examples

$0.333\ldots = 0.\dot{3}$

$0.17777\ldots = 0.1\dot{7}$

$0.232323\ldots = 0.\dot{2}\dot{3}$

Ordering decimals

When ordering decimals:

- first write them with the same number of figures after the decimal point;
- then compare whole numbers, digits in the tenths place, digits in the hundredths place, and so on.

Example

Arrange these numbers in order of size, smallest first:

6.21, 6.023, 6.4, 6.04, 2.71, 9.4

First rewrite them:

6.210, 6.023, 6.400, 6.040, 2.710, 9.400

Then re-order them:

2.710, 6.023, 6.040, 6.210, 6.400, 9.400

Always check that all values have been included.

Rounding numbers

Decimal places (d.p.)

When rounding numbers to a specified number of decimal places:

- look at the last number that is wanted (if rounding 12.367 to 2 d.p., look at the 6 (second d.p.));
- look at the number next to it (look at the number not needed – the 7);
- if it is **5 or more**, then **round up** the last digit (7 is greater than 5, so round the 6 up to a 7);
- if it is **less than 5**, the digit remains the **same**.

Examples

Round 12.49 to 1 d.p.

12.4**9** rounds up to 12.5.

Round 8.735 to 2 d.p.

8.73**5** rounds up to 8.74.

Round 9.624 to 2 d.p.

9.62**4** rounds to 9.62.

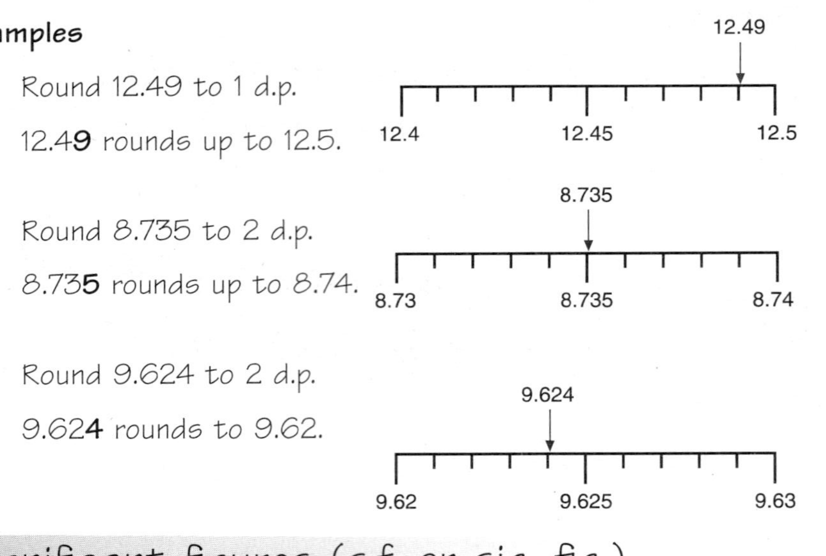

Significant figures (s.f. or sig. fig.)

Apply the same rule as with decimal places: if the next digit is 5 or more, round up.

The 1st significant figure is the first digit which is not a zero. The 2nd, 3rd, 4th, . . . significant figures follow on after the 1st digit. They may or may not be zeros.

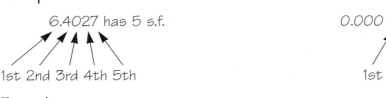

Take care when rounding that you do not change the place values.

Examples

Examples

Number	to 3 s.f.	to 2 s.f.	to 1 s.f.
4.207	4.21	4.2	4
4379	4380	4400	4000
0.006 209	0.006 21	0.0062	0.006

After rounding the last digit, you must fill in the end zeros. For example, 4380 = 4400 to 2 s.f. (not 44).

Percentages

These are fractions with a denominator of 100. For example 75% = $\frac{75}{100}$.

Ratios

A ratio is used to **compare** two or more related quantities.

A colon : is used to mean 'compared to'. For example, '16 boys compared to 20 girls' is written as '16:20'.

To **simplify** ratios, use the calculator fraction key.

- Make a table of values.

x	-2	-1	0	1	2	3	0.5
y	0	-4	-6	-6	-4	0	-6.25

$x = 0.5$ is worked out to find the minimum value.

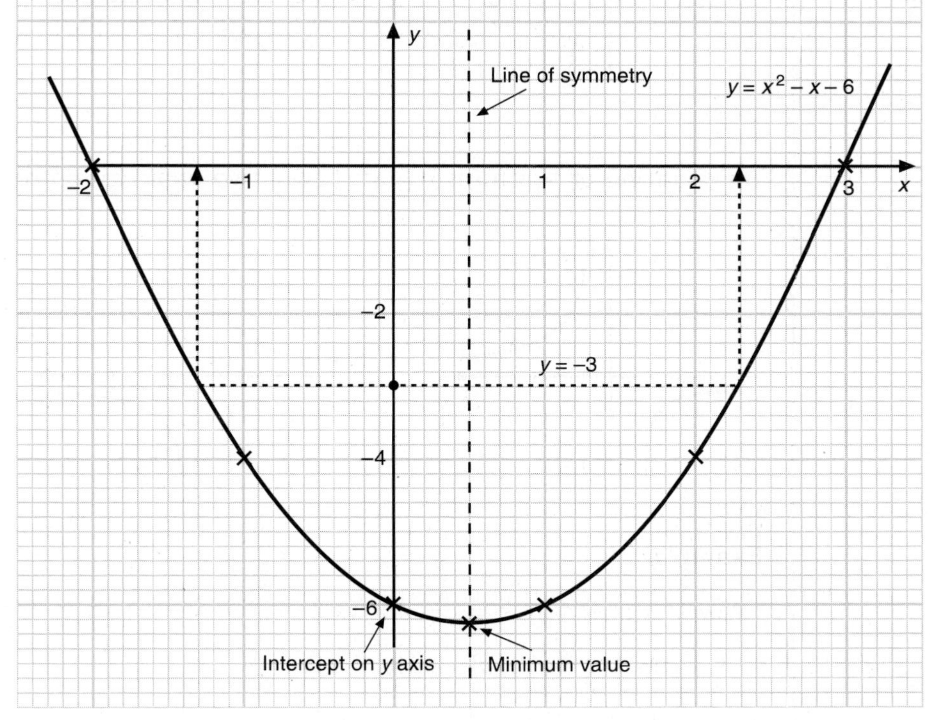

Draw the curve with a sharp pencil, go through all the points and check for any points that look wrong.

- Plot the points and join with a smooth curve.
- The minimum value is when $x = 0.5$, $y = -6.25$.
- The line of symmetry is at $x = 0.5$.
- The curve cuts the y axis at $(0, -6)$, i.e. $(0, c)$.
- When $y = -3$, read across from $y = -3$ to the graph then read up to the x axis. $x = 2.3$ and $x = -1.3$. These are the approximate **solutions** of the equation $x^2 - x - 6 = -3$.

Graphs involving x^3 and $1/x$

An equation of the form $y = ax^3 + bx^2 + cx + d$ is called a **cubic** where $a \neq 0$.

For $a > 0$ the graph of a cubic takes one of these forms.

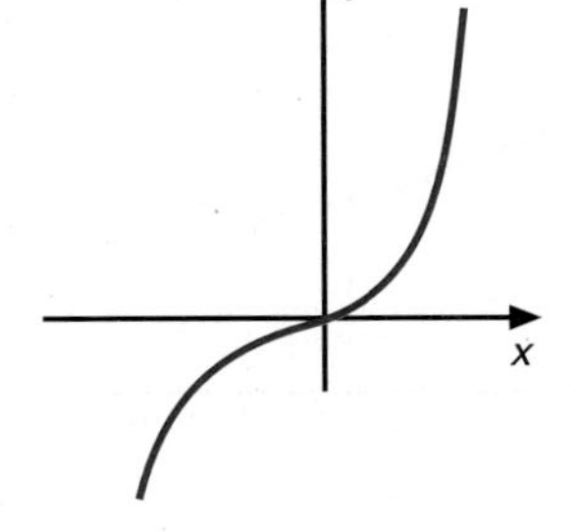

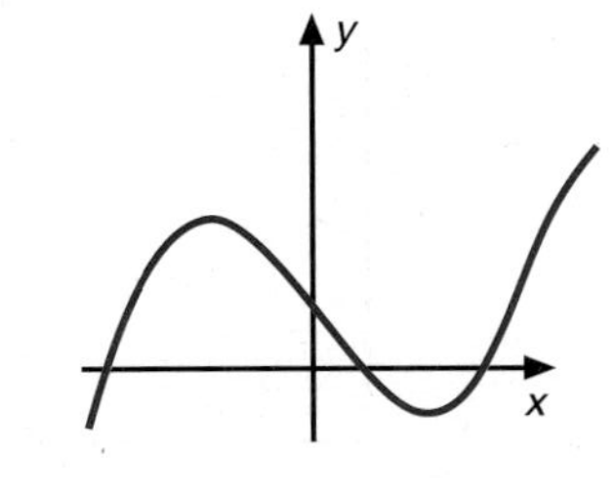

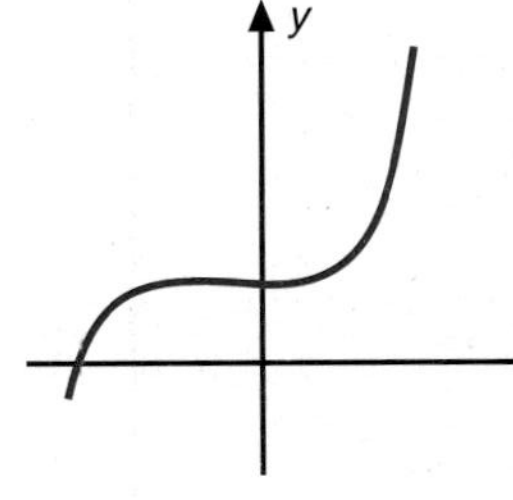

The basic shapes of all of these graphs need to be learnt.

For $a < 0$ the overall trend is reversed.

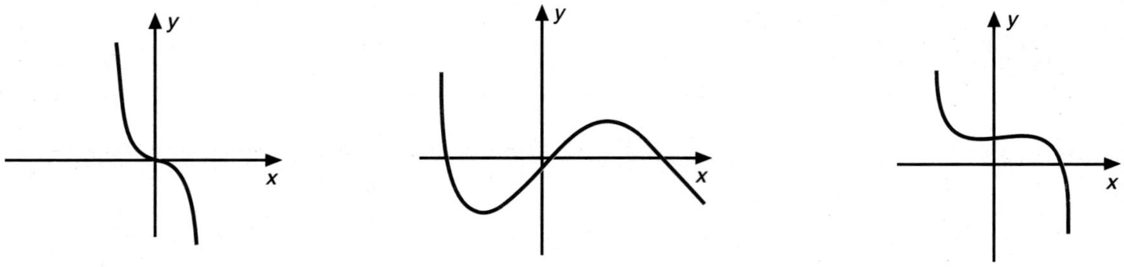

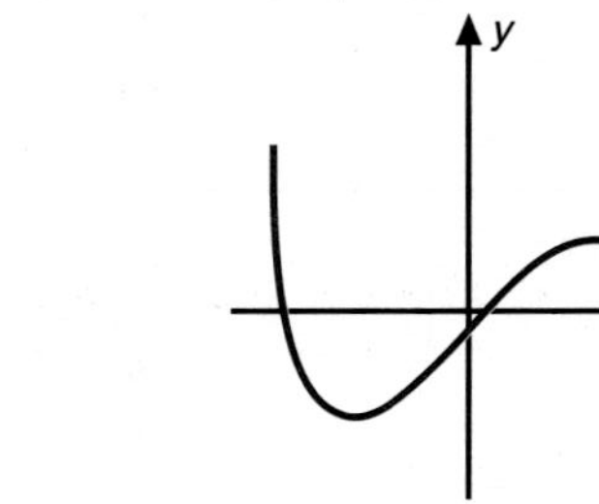

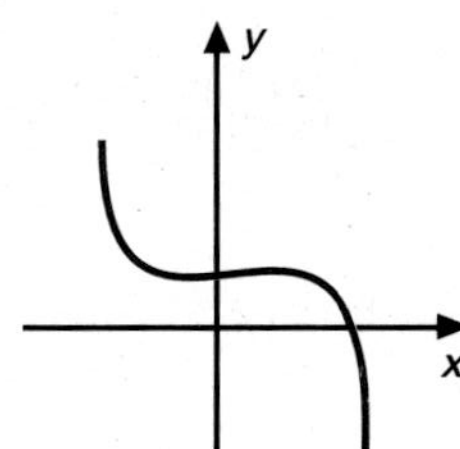

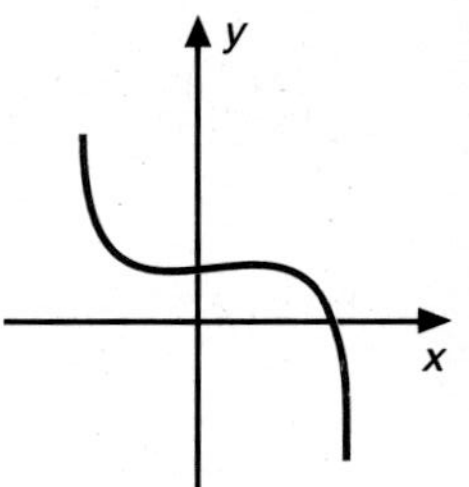

An equation of the form $y = \frac{a}{x}$ takes two basic forms depending on the value of a.

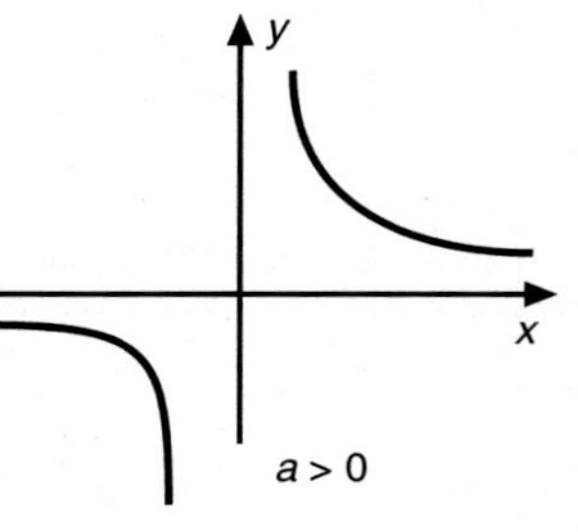

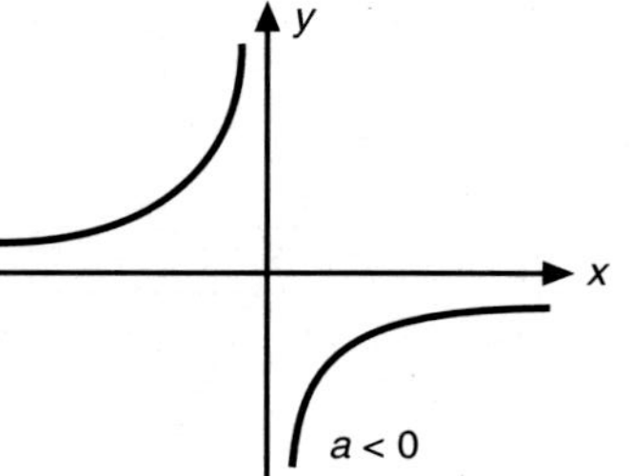

Example

Draw the graph of $P = \frac{18}{V}$ for values of V from 1 to 6. Find the value of V if $P = 8$.

- Draw the table of values first.

V	1	2	3	4	5	6
P	18	9	6	4.5	3.6	3

- Find the values of P by dividing 18 by V.
- Draw a smooth curve through the points.
- To find V when $P = 8$ read across at $P = 8$ then draw a line down. $V \approx 2.24$.

Show clearly on your graph how you have taken the reading.

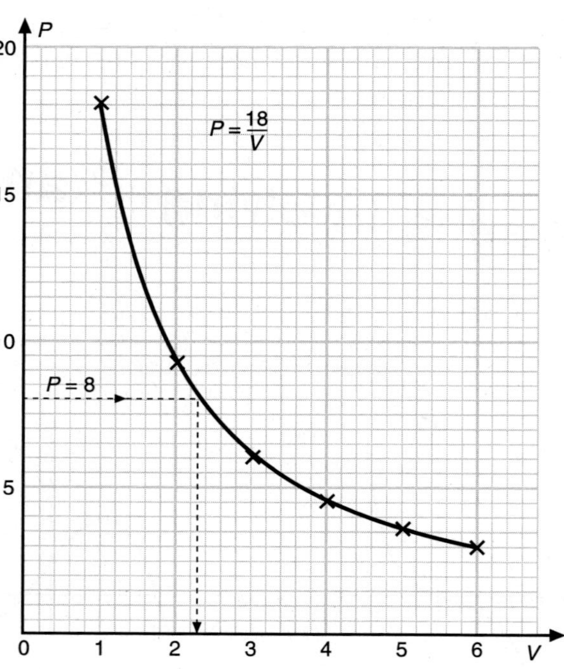

Questions

1 If $a = 3.6$, $b = -2.4$ and $c = 6.1$, find the value of these expressions giving your answers to 3 significant figures.

(a) $3a - 4b$ (b) $2b^2 + 3c$

(c) ab^2 (d) $c + \frac{a}{b}$

2 Find the nth term of these sequences: (a) 5, 9, 13, 17 (b) 3, 6, 11, 18

3 Write down the gradient and intercept of each of these straight line graphs:

(a) $y = 4x - 1$ (b) $y = 3 - 2x$ (c) $2y = 4x + 8$

4 The travel graph shows the car journeys of two people. From the travel graph find:

(a) the speed at which Miss Young is travelling;

(b) the length of time Mr Price has a break;

(c) the speed of Mr Price from London to Birmingham;

(d) the time at which Miss Young and Mr Price pass each other.

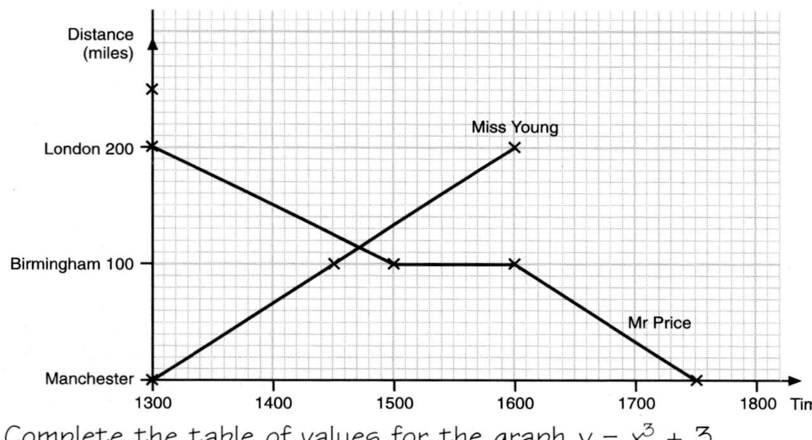

5 (a) Complete the table of values for the graph $y = x^3 + 3$.

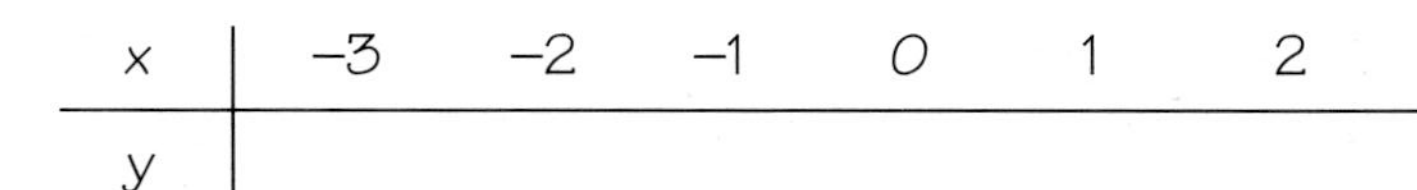

x	−3	−2	−1	0	1	2	3
y							

(b) Draw the graph of $y = x^3 + 3$. Use scales of 1 unit per 2 cm on the x axis and 10 units per 2 cm on the y axis.

(c) From the graph find the value of x when $y = 15$.

6 Match each of the four graphs below with one of the following equations:

(a) $y = 2x - 5$ (b) $y = x^2 + 3$ (c) $y = 3 - x^2$ (d) $y = 5 - x$ (e) $y = x^3$ (f) $y = \frac{2}{x}$

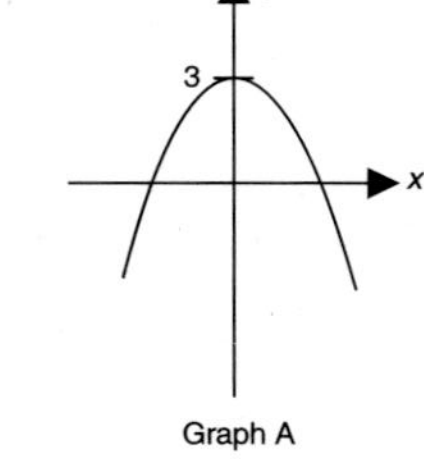

Graph A

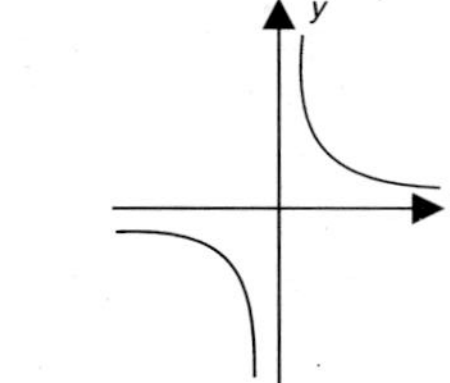

Graph B

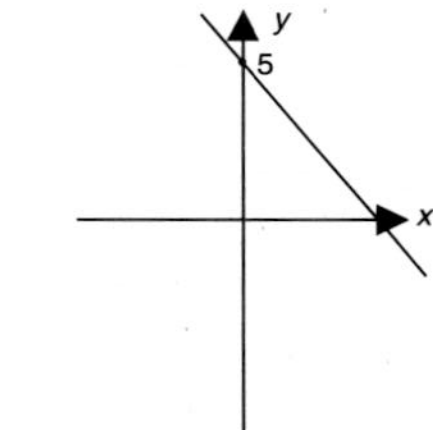

Graph C

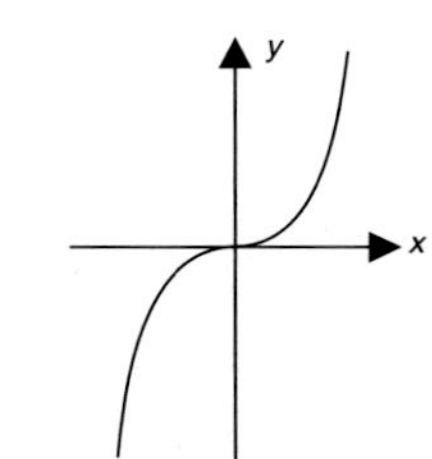

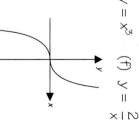

Graph D

Equations and formulae

Algebraic conventions

Examiner's tips and your notes

$3 \times a$ is written without the multiplication sign as $3a$.

$a + a + a = 3a$

$a \times a \times a = a^3$, not $3a$

$a \times a \times 2 = 2a^2$, not $(2a)^2$

$a \times b \times 2 = 2ab$

Put the number first, then the letters in alphabetical order.

Using formulae

Formulae describe expressions. A formula must have an = sign in it.

Example
Andrew hires a van. There is a standing charge of £8 and then it costs £3 per hour. How much does it cost for:

(a) 6 hours' hire; (b) y hours' hire?

(c) Write a formula for the total hire cost C.

(a) $8 + (3 \times 6) = £26$

(b) $8 + (3 \times y) = 8 + 3y$

(c) $C = 8 + 3y$

Make sure you include an equals sign in your formula.

This is a formula which works out the cost of hiring the van for any number of hours.

Collecting like terms

Expressions can be simplified by collecting **like terms**.

Only collect the terms if their letters and powers are **identical**.

Examples

$4a + 2a = 6a$

$3a^2 + 6a^2 - 4a^2 = 5a^2$

$4a + 6b - 3a + 2b = a + 8b$

Add the *a*s, then the *b*s. Remember *a* means 1*a*.

$9a + 4b$ cannot be simplified since there are no like terms.

$3xy + 2yx = 5xy$

Remember *xy* means the same as *yx*.

Indices

The rules that apply with numbers also apply with letters.

The laws of indices

These rules are not given on the formulae sheet in the examination and so they must be learnt.

$a^n \times a^m = a^{n+m}$ $a^n \div a^m = a^{n-m}$ $(a^n)^m = a^{n \times m}$ $a^0 = 1$ $a^1 = a$

Examples

$4x^2 \times 3x^5 = 12x^7$ $15x^9 \div 3x^2 = 5x^7$ $(2x^4)^3 = 8x^{12}$

Note that the numbers are multiplied, . . .

. . . but the powers of the same letter are added.

Multiplying out brackets

This helps to simplify algebraic expressions.

Multiply everything inside the bracket by everything outside the bracket.

If you are asked to expand brackets it just means multiply out.

$a(b + c - d) = ab + ac - ad$

Examples

$3(2x + 5) = 6x + 15$ $(3 \times 2x = 6x, 3 \times 5 = 15)$

$a(3a - 4) = 3a^2 - 4a$ $b(2a + 3b - c) = 2ab + 3b^2 - bc$

If the term outside the bracket is **negative**, all of the signs of the terms inside the bracket are **changed** when multiplying out.

Remember the rules for multiplying by negative numbers.

Examples

$-4(2x + 3) = -8x - 12$ $-2(4 - 3x) = -8 + 6x$

To simplify expressions expand the brackets first then collect like terms.

Example

Expand and simplify $2(x - 3) + x(x + 4)$.

$2(x - 3) + x(x + 4)$ Multiply out the brackets.

$= 2x - 6 + x^2 + 4x$ Collect like terms.

$= x^2 + 6x - 6$

Multiplication of two brackets

Each term in the first bracket is multiplied with *each* term in the *second* bracket.

If you are asked to simplify you must collect like terms.

Examples

Expand and simplify the following.

(a) $(x + 2)(x + 3)$ $= x(x + 3) + 2(x + 3)$

$= x^2 + 3x + 2x + 6$

$= x^2 + 5x + 6$

Each term in the first bracket is multiplied with the second, simplify by collecting like terms.

(b) $(2x + 4)(3x - 2)$ $= 2x(3x - 2) + 4(3x - 2)$

$= 6x^2 - 4x + 12x - 8$

$= 6x^2 + 8x - 8$

(c) $(x + y)^2$ $= x(x + y) + y(x + y)$

$= x^2 + xy + xy + y^2$

$= x^2 + 2xy + y^2$

A common error is to think that $(a + b)^2$ means $a^2 + b^2$.

Factorisation

This is the *reverse* of *expanding* brackets. An *expression* is put into brackets by taking out **common factors**.

One bracket

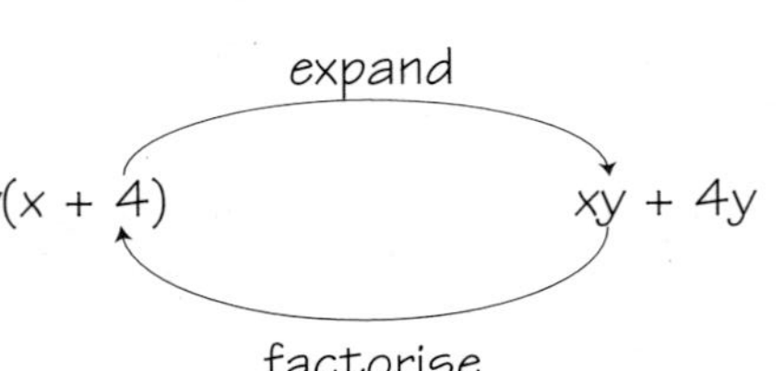

To factorise $xy + 4y$:

- recognise that y is a factor of *each* term;
- take out the common factor;
- the expression is completed inside the bracket, so that the result is *equivalent* to $xy + 4y$, when multiplied out.

After factorising check that you obtain the original expression by multiplying out the brackets.

Examples

Factorise the following.

(a) $5x^2 + x = x\,(5x + 1)$

(b) $4x^2 + 8x = 4x(x + 2)$

Highest factor of 4 and 8 is taken out.

(c) $5x^3 + 15x^4 = 5x^3(1 + 3x)$

Two brackets

Two brackets are obtained when a quadratic expression of the type $x^2 + bx + c$ is factorised.

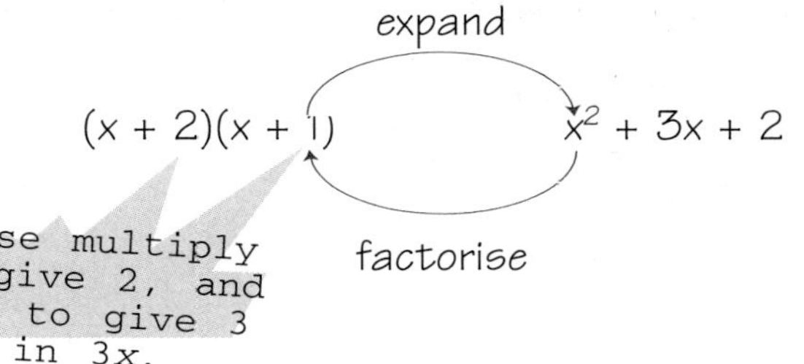

Examples

Factorise the following.

(a) $x^2 + 5x - 6 = (x - 1)(x + 6)$

(b) $x^2 - 6x + 8 = (x - 2)(x - 4)$

(c) $x^2 - 16 = (x - 4)(x + 4)$

Rearranging formulae

The **subject** of a formula is the letter that appears on its own on one side of the formula.

Examples

Make p the subject of these formulae: (a) $r = (p + 6)^2$ (b) $y = \frac{p + r}{6}$

(a) $r = (p + 6)^2$ Deal with the power first. Take the square root of both sides.

$\sqrt{r} = p + 6$ Remove any terms added or subtracted. So subtract 6 from both sides.

$\sqrt{r} - 6 = p$

Remember to show each step in your working.

(b) $y = \frac{p + r}{6}$ Deal with the value dividing with p; multiply both sides by 6.

$6y = p + r$ Remove r by subtracting r from both sides.

$6y - r = p$ or $p = 6y - r$

The subject of the formula is usually written first.

Linear equations

An equation involves an unknown value which has to be worked out.

The **balance** method is usually used; whatever is done to one side of an equation must be done to the other.

'Solve' means 'work out'.

Check by substituting back into the original equation.

Examples

Solve the following.

(a) $\frac{x}{6} + 1 = 3$

$\frac{x}{6} = 3 - 1$ Subtract 1 from both sides.

$\frac{x}{6} = 2$ Multiply both sides by 6.

$x = 12$

(b) $8x - 6 = 4x + 1$

$4x - 6 = 1$ Subtract 4x from both sides.

$4x = 7$ Add 6 to both sides.

$x = \frac{7}{4} = 1\frac{3}{4}$ Divide both sides by 4.

(c) $3(x - 2) = 2(x + 6)$ Multiply brackets out first.

$3x - 6 = 2x + 12$

$x - 6 = 12$

$x = 18$

(d) $5(x - 2) + 6 = 3(x - 4) + 10$

$5x - 10 + 6 = 3x - 12 + 10$

$5x - 4 = 3x - 2$

$2x - 4 = -2$

$2x = 2$

$x = 1$

Simultaneous equations

Two equations with two unknowns are called **simultaneous equations**.

They can be solved in several ways. Solving equations simultaneously involves finding values for the letters that will make both equations work.

Graphical method

The points at which any two graphs **intersect** represent the simultaneous solutions of these equations.

Example

Solve the simultaneous equations $y = 2x - 1$, $x + y = 5$

- Draw the two graphs.

$y = 2x - 1$ If $x = 0$, $y = -1$
If $y = 0$, $x = \frac{1}{2}$

$x + y = 5$ If $x = 0$, $y = 5$
If $y = 0$, $x = 5$

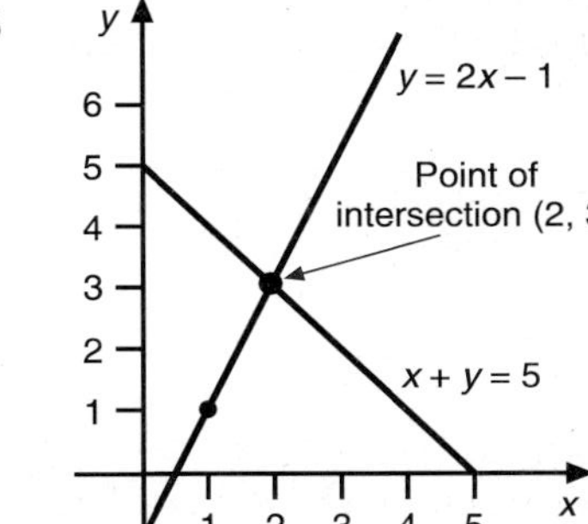

- At the point of intersection $x = 2$ and $y = 3$.
These values represent the simultaneous solutions of $y = 2x - 1$ and $x + y = 5$

Elimination method

If the coefficient of one of the letters is the same in both equations, then that letter may be eliminated by subtracting the equations.

The **coefficient** is the number a letter is multiplied by; e.g. the coefficient of $-2x$ is -2.

Example

Solve simultaneously $2x + 3y = 6$ and $x + y = 1$

$2x + 3y = 6$	①	Label the equations ① and ②.
$x + y = 1$	②	As no coefficients match, multiply equation ② by 2.
$2x + 2y = 2$	③	The coefficients of x are now the same in equations ① and ③.
$0x + y = 4$		Subtract equation ③ from equation ①.
So $y = 4$		
$x + 4 = 1$ so $x = -3$		Substitute the value of $y = 4$ into equation ① or equation ②.

Always check that the values work.

Check in equation 1: $(2 \times -3) + (3 \times 4) = 6$

Substitute $x = -3$ and $y = 4$ into the other equation.

The solution is $x = -3$, $y = 4$

To eliminate terms with **opposite** signs, **add**.

To eliminate terms with the **same** signs, **subtract**.

Solving quadratic equations

Make sure the quadratic equation is equal to zero. Then factorise the quadratic equation.

Examples
Solve the following.

(a) $x^2 - 5x = 0$ x is a common factor.
$x(x - 5) = 0$
Either $x = 0$
or $x - 5 = 0$, i.e. $x = 5$

In order for this to be zero, either $x = 0$ or $(x - 5) = 0$

(b) $x^2 - 3x = 10$
$x^2 - 3x - 10 = 0$ Make it equal to zero and factorise.
$(x + 2)(x - 5) = 0$
Either $(x + 2) = 0$ i.e. $x = -2$
or $(x - 5) = 0$ i.e. $x = 5$

Solving cubic equations by trial and improvement

Trial and improvement gives an approximate solution to equations. It involves a systematic search, whereby selected values are substituted into one side of the equation in order to reach some target figure on the other.

Example

The equation $x^3 - 5x = 10$ has a solution between 2 and 3. Find this solution to 2 decimal places.

Draw a table to help.

Substitute different values of x into $x^3 - 5x$.

Make sure you write down the solution of x, not the answer to $x^3 - 5x$.

x	$x^3 - 5x$	Comment
2.5	3.125	too small
2.8	7.952	too small
2.9	9.889	too small
2.95	10.922375	too big
2.94	10.712184	too big
2.91	10.092171	too big

At this stage the solution is trapped between 2.90 and 2.91. Checking the middle value $x = 2.905$ gives $x^3 - 5x = 9.99036 \ldots$ which is too small.

2.90 (too small) — 2.905 (too small) — 2.91 (too big)

The diagram makes it clear that the solution is 2.91 correct to 2 decimal places.

Inequalities

These are expressions where one side is **not equal** to the other.

Inequalities are solved in a similar way to equations.

$<$ 'is less than',
$>$ 'is greater than'
$\leq$ 'is less than or equal to'
$\geq$ 'is greater than or equal to'

Multiplying and dividing by **negative numbers** changes the **direction** of the sign. For example if $-x \geq 5$ then $x \leq -5$.

Solve inequalities in a similar way to equations.

Examples

Solve the following inequalities.

(a) $4x - 2 < 2x + 6$

$2x - 2 < 6$ Subtract $2x$ from both sides.

$2x < 8$ Add 2 to both sides.

$x < 4$ Divide both sides by 2.

The solution of the inequality may be represented on a number line.

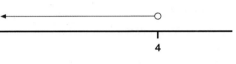

4

Use • when the end point is included and ∘ when the end point is not included.

(b) $-5 < 3x + 1 \leq 13$ Subtract 1 from each side.

$-6 < 3x \leq 12$ Divide by 3.

$-2 < x \leq 4$

The **integer values** which satisfy the above inequality are −1, 0, 1, 2, 3, 4.

Graphs of inequalities

The graph of an equation such as $y = 3$ is a line, whereas the graph of the inequality $y < 3$ is a **region** which has the line $y = 3$ as its **boundary**.

To show the region for given inequalities:

- Draw the boundary lines first.
- For **strict** inequalities > and < the boundary line is not included and is shown as a dotted line.
- It is often easier with several inequalities to *shade out the unwanted regions*, so that the solution is shown **unshaded**.

Example

The diagram shows unshaded the region $x > 1$, $x + y \leq 4$, $y \geq 0$

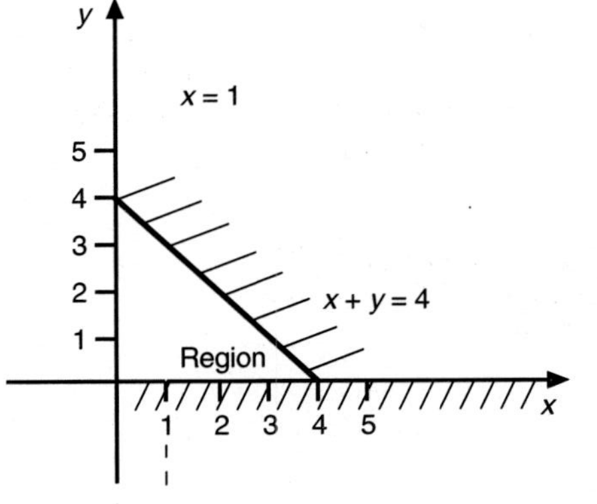

Equations and formulae

Questions

1 Simplify:

(a) $4x^2 \times 5x^3$ (b) $6x^{13} \div 2x^9$

(c) $(4x^3)^2$ (d) x^0

2 Expand and simplify:

(a) $2(x - 6) + 3x(x - 2)$ (b) $(x + 6)(x - 2)$

(c) $(x - 6)^2$ (d) $(2x + y)(3x - 2)$

3 Factorise the following expressions.

(a) $pq + qr$ (b) $5x^2 + 10x^3y$

(c) $x^2 - 5x + 4$ (d) $x^2 - 64$

4 Make *a* the subject of each formula.

(a) $r = 5a$ (b) $r = \sqrt{4a + b}$ (c) $r = 4q - 2a$

5 Solve the following equations.

(a) $4x - 3 = 9$ (b) $6x + 3 = 2x + 9$

(c) $5(x - 4) = 3(x - 6)$ (d) $\frac{500}{x} = 10$

6 Solve the simultaneous equations: $3a + b = 5$

$2a + 3b = 1$

7 Solve these quadratic equations.

(a) $x^2 - 7x = 0$ (b) $x^2 = 9x - 20$

8 Solve these inequalities.

(a) $5x - 1 \leq 2x + 9$ (b) $-4 < 2x - 6 \leq 10$

Shape, space and measures

Properties of shapes

Symmetry

Examiner's tips and your notes

Reflective symmetry

Both sides of a symmetrical shape are the same when the mirror line is drawn across it. The mirror line is known as the **line** or **axis of symmetry**.

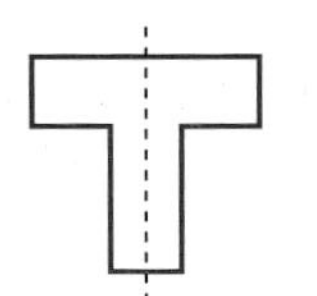
1 line

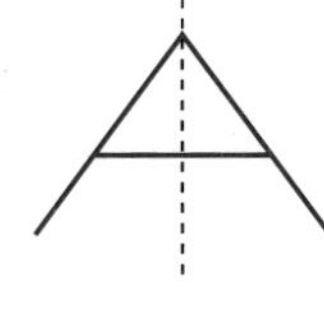
1 line

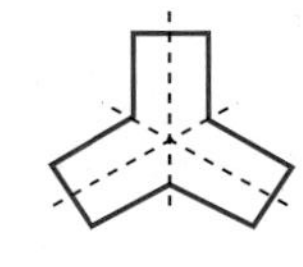
3 lines

No lines

Rotational symmetry

A 2D (two-dimensional) shape has rotational symmetry, if, when it is turned, it looks exactly the same. The **order of rotational symmetry** is the number of times the shape turns and looks the same.

You may be asked to complete a shape to make it symmetrical.

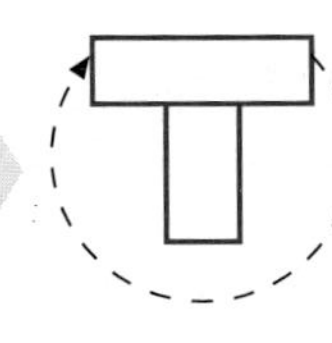
Order 1

Order 1

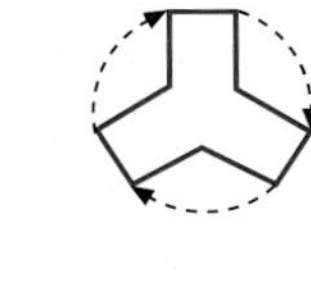
Order 3

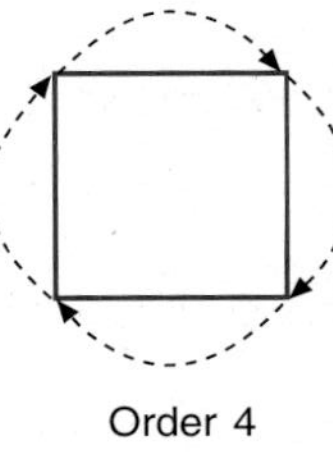
Order 4

For the letter M the shape has 1 position. It is said to have **rotational symmetry of order 1**, or **no** rotational symmetry.

Plane symmetry

This is symmetry in 3D (three-dimensional) solids only.

A 3D shape has a **plane of symmetry** if the plane divides the shape into two halves, and one half is an exact mirror image of the other.

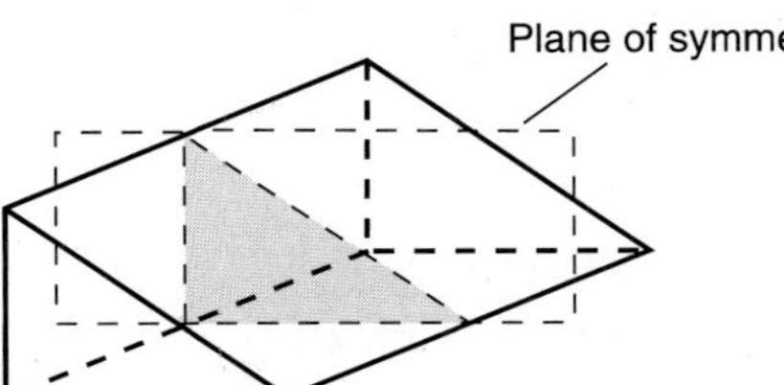

2D shapes

Triangles

There are several types of triangle.

Equilateral

3 sides equal
3 angles equal

Isosceles

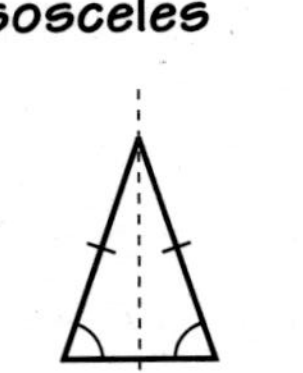

2 sides equal
base angles equal

Right-angled

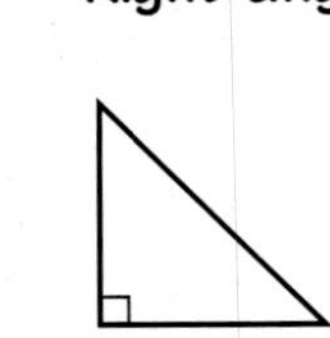

has a 90° angle

Scalene

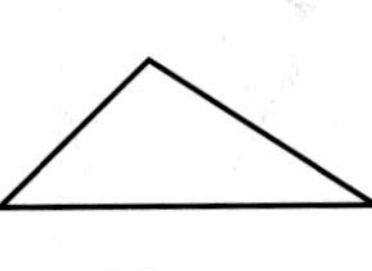

no sides or angles the same

Quadrilaterals

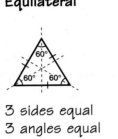

You must learn the names of these shapes and their symmetrical properties.

These are four-sided shapes.

Square

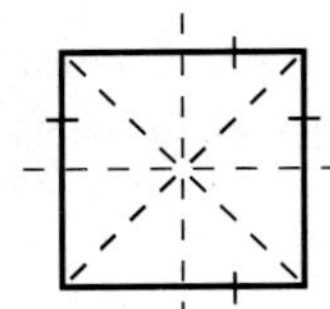

4 lines of symmetry
rotational symmetry of order 4

Rectangle

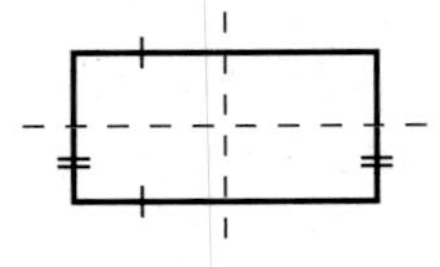

2 lines of symmetry
rotational symmetry of order 2

Parallelogram

no lines of symmetry
rotational symmetry of order 2

Rhombus

2 lines of symmetry
rotational symmetry of order 2

Kite

1 line of symmetry
no rotational symmetry

Trapezium

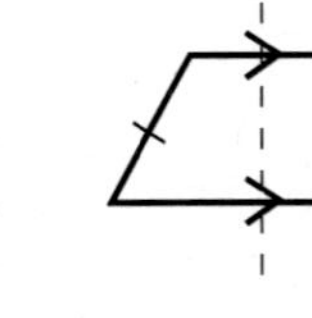

isosceles trapezium:
1 line of symmetry
no rotational symmetry

To order see the back page

Questions

1 Change 3500 g into kg.

2 Change 3 stone into pounds.

3 Change 6 litres into pints.

4 Write down the upper and lower limits for a time of 9.2 seconds, rounded to the nearest tenth of a second.

5 Work out the area of the following shapes, giving your answers to 3 s.f.

(a)

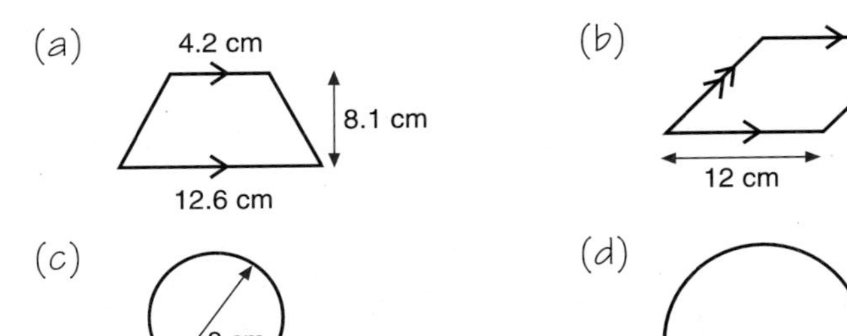

(b)

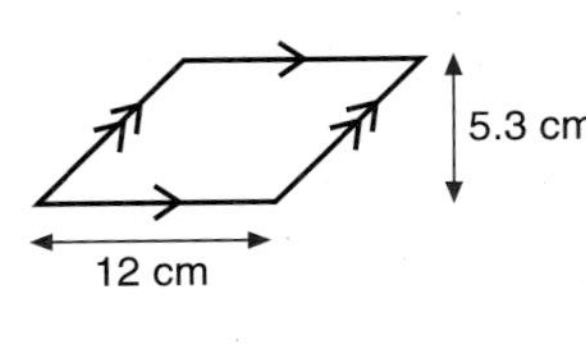

(c)

(d)

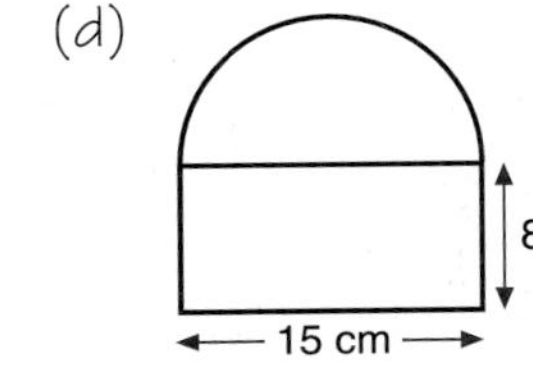

6 Work out the volume of the following 3D shapes. Give your answer to 3 s.f.

(a)

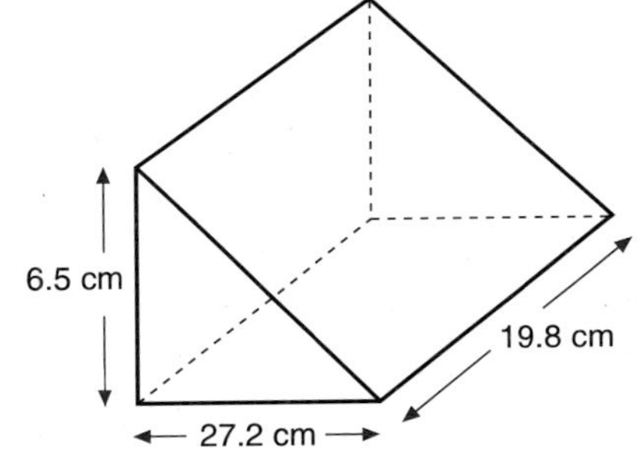

(b)

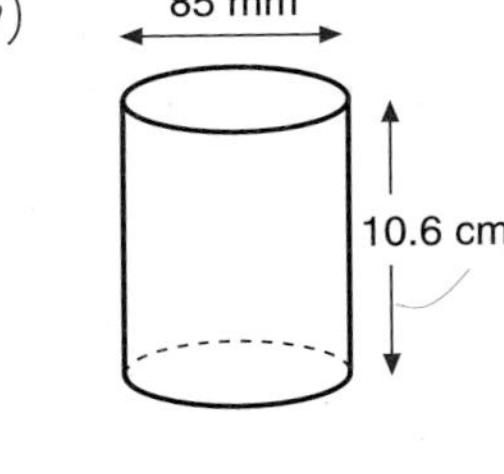

7 The volume of a cylinder is 2000 cm^3 and the radius is 5.6 cm. Work out the height to 3 s.f.

8 x, y, z represent lengths. For each expression write down whether it could represent perimeter, area or volume.

(a) $\sqrt{x^2 + y^2 + z^2}$ (b) $\frac{5}{9}\pi x^3 + 2y^3$

(c) $\frac{1}{3}\frac{xyz^2}{y}$ (d) $\frac{9}{5}\pi xy + \frac{4}{5}\pi yz$

Processing and interpreting data

Types of data

Examiner's tips and your notes

- **Quantitative** – The answer is a **number**; e.g. how many red cars are in the car park?
- **Qualitative** – The answer is a **word**; e.g. what is your favourite colour?
- **Discrete data** – Each category is separate. It is often found by counting. Examples include the number of people with blue eyes.
- **Continuous data** – Here the values change from one category to the next. Such data is often found by measuring. Examples include heights and weights of Year 9 pupils.

Hypotheses, experiments and questionnaires

A **hypothesis** is a prediction which can be tested.

Experiments

Experiments are used to test hypotheses. They may contain several variables.

Example

Hypothesis – 'The better the light, the more the seedlings grow.'

Variable – This is the intensity of the light which will be changed.

Conditions – The other conditions must stay the same. All seedlings must be exactly the same size, strength and colour. If there is **bias** (e.g. one side of the tray gets extra sunlight) then the experiment has to start again.

Questionnaires

Questionnaires can be used to test hypotheses.

When designing questionnaires:

- Decide what needs to be found out, the 'hypotheses'.
- Give instructions on how the questionnaire has to be filled in.
- Do not ask for information which is not needed (e.g. name).
- Make the questions clear and concise.

You may be asked to criticise some examples of questions used in a questionnaire or to provide some of your own.

Word any questions you write very carefully.

- Keep the questionnaire short.
- If people's opinion is needed, make sure the question is **unbiased**. An example of a biased question would be: 'Do you agree that a leisure centre should have a tennis court rather than a squash court?'
- Allow for any possible answers – for example:

  How many hours (to the nearest hour) a day do you watch TV?

  0–2 ☐ 3–5 ☐ 6–8 ☐ More than 8 ☐

Pie charts

These are used to illustrate data. They are circles split into sections, each section representing a certain number of items.

Calculating angles for a pie chart

- Find the total for the items listed.
- Find the fraction of the total for each item.
- Multiply the fraction by 360° to find the angle.

Example

The hair colour of 24 ten-year-olds:

Hair colour	Frequency
Brown	8
Auburn	4
Blonde	6
Black	6
	Total = 24

Key in on the calculator

8 ÷ 24 × 360 =

Finding the angle

Brown $= \frac{8}{24} \times 360° = 120°$

Auburn $= \frac{4}{24} \times 360° = 60°$

Blonde $= \frac{6}{24} \times 360° = 90°$

Black $= \frac{6}{24} \times 360° = 90°$

Total $= 360°$

Check that the angles add up to 360°.

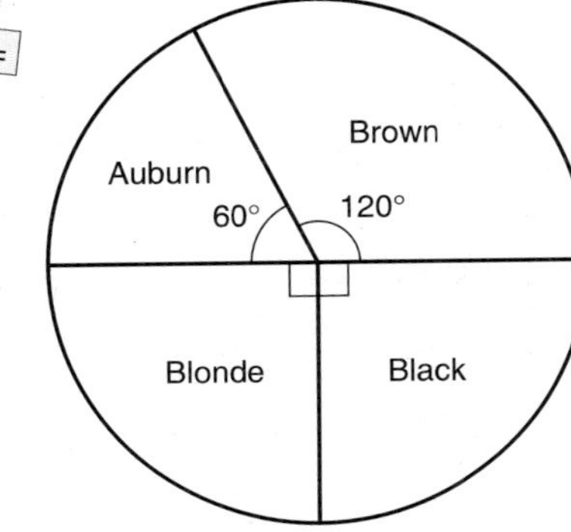

Interpreting pie charts

Example

The pie chart shows the number of pupils choosing different options. If 48 choose Art, how many choose Technology?

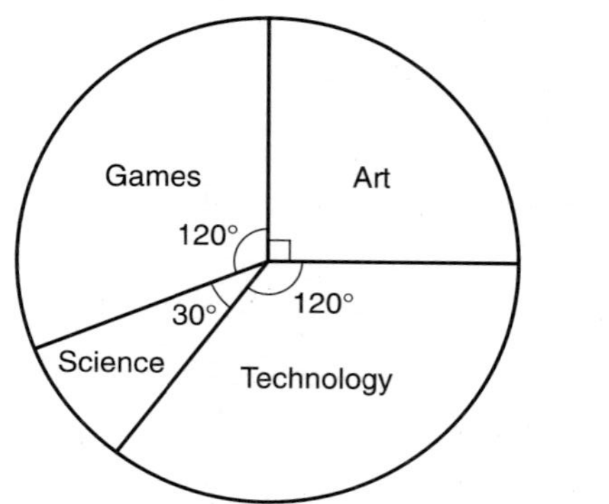

Check that your answers seem sensible.

90° represents 48 pupils

1° represents $\frac{48}{90} = 0.53\dot{3}$ pupils

Technology = $120 \times 0.53\dot{3} = 64$ pupils

(120 lots of $0.53\dot{3}$)

Make sure that this number is not rounded off!

Line graphs

These are a set of points joined by lines.

Year	1988	1989	1990	1991	1992	1993
Number of cars sold	2500	2900	2100	1900	1600	800

Middle values, like point A, have no meaning. A does **not** mean that halfway between 1990 and 1991, there were 2000 cars sold.

Histograms

These are drawn to illustrate **continuous data**. They are similar to bar charts except there are no gaps between the bars. The data must be grouped into **equal** class intervals if the length of the bar is used to represent the frequency.

Example

The weights of 30 workers in a factory are shown in the table.

Weight (kg)	Frequency
$45 \le w < 55$	7
$55 \le w < 65$	13
$65 \le w < 75$	6
$75 \le w < 85$	4
	30

$45 \le w < 55$, etc. are called **class intervals** – they are all equal in width.

$55 \le w < 65$ means the weights are between 55 kg and 65 kg.

$55 \le$ means that w can be equal to 55 kg, while
< 65 means that w cannot be equal to 65 kg (it would be in the next group).

Note:

- The axes do not need to start at zero.
- The axes are labelled.
- The graph has a title.

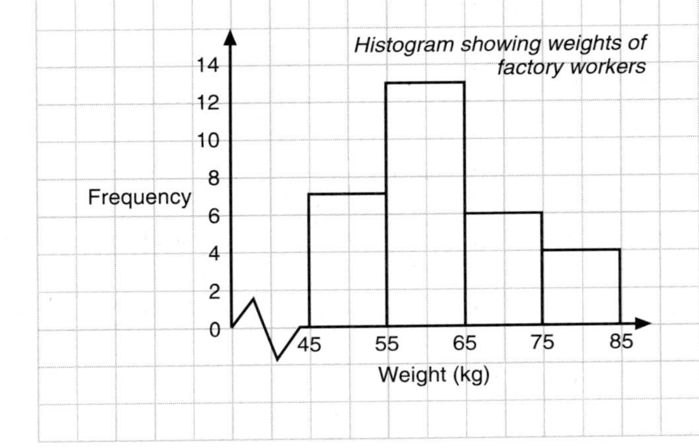

…f the scale on either axis …oesn't start at …ero then attention should be drawn to this …act by using a …agged line like

Frequency polygons

These are used to join the **midpoints of class intervals** for grouped or continuous data.

Consider the histogram of the factory workers again.

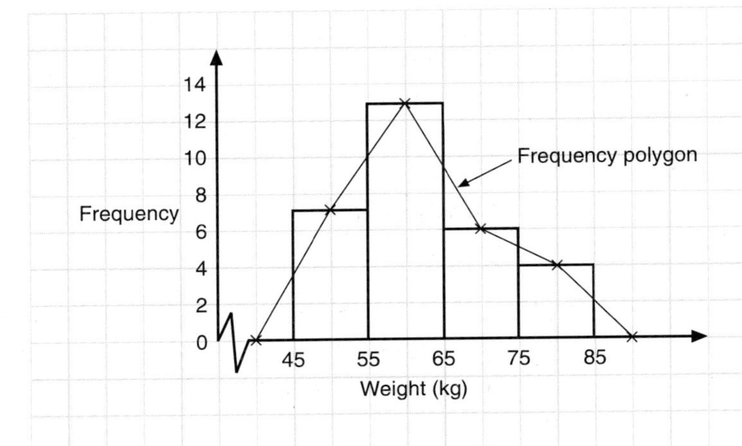

For a frequency polygon remember to plot at the midpoints of the class intervals.

A frequency polygon is said to show the **trend** of the data.

To draw the frequency polygon:

- Put a cross on the middle of each bar.
- Join the crosses up with a ruler.
- Draw the line from the midpoint on the first bar to the x axis which is half a class interval before the first bar.
- Draw the line from the midpoint on the last bar to the x axis which is half a class interval after the last bar.

Scatter diagrams

A scatter diagram (scatter graph or scatter plot) is used to show two sets of data at the same time.

Its importance is to show the **correlation** (connection) between two sets of data. There are three types of correlation: positive, negative or zero.

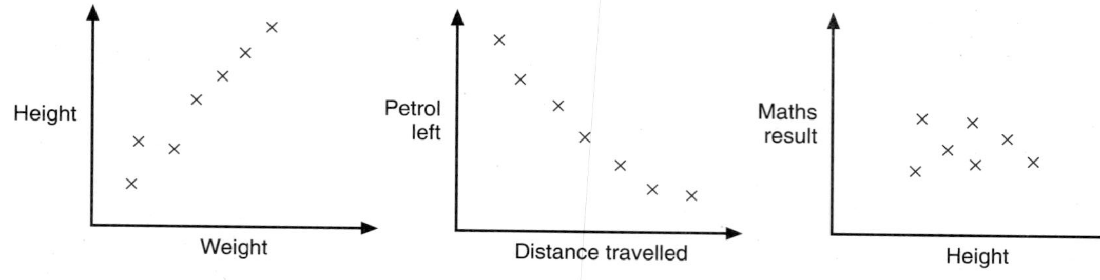

Positive – This is when both variables are increasing. If the points are nearly a straight line it is said to have a **high positive correlation**.

Negative – This is when one variable increases whilst the other decreases. The one above has a **high negative correlation**.

Zero – This is when there is little or no correlation between the variables.

Drawing a scatter diagram

Do not rush when drawing a scatter diagram, otherwise you will plot the points incorrectly.

- Work out the scales first.
- Plot the points carefully.
- Each time a point is plotted, tick them off.

Example

Maths test (%)	64	79	38	42	49	75	83	82	66	61	54
History test (%)	70	36	84	70	74	42	29	33	50	56	64

The table shows the maths and history results of 11 pupils.

The scatter diagram overleaf shows there is a **strong negative correlation** – in general, the better the pupils did in maths, the worse they did in history, and vice versa.

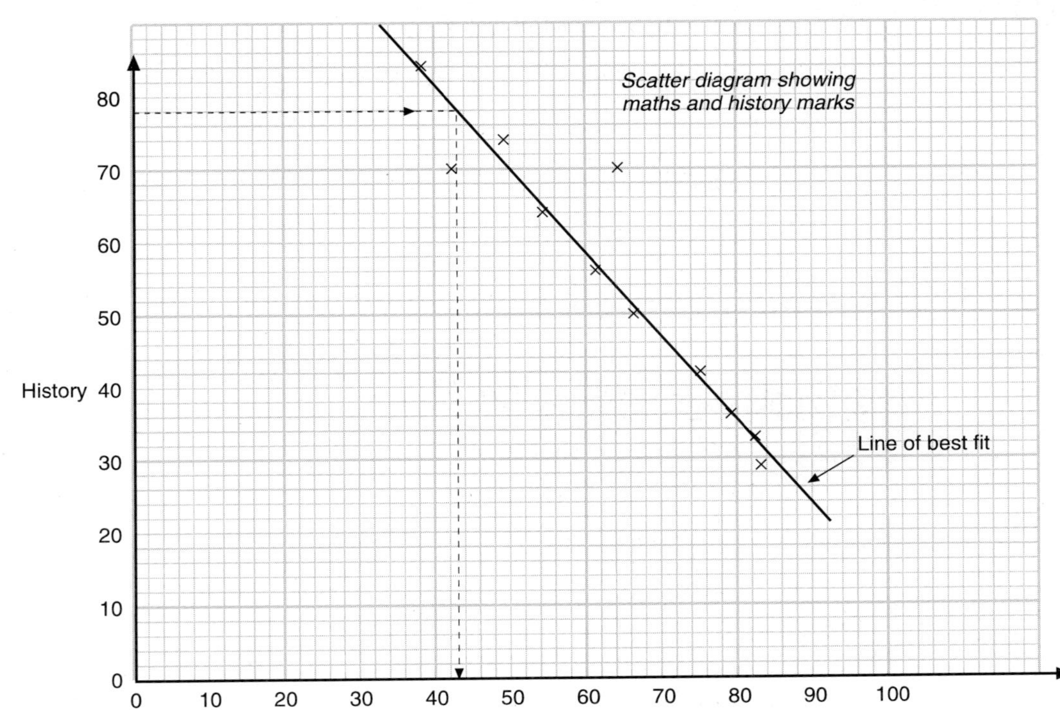

Line of best fit

Draw your line in pencil carefully.

This is the line which best fits the data. It goes in the direction of the data and has roughly the same number of points above the line as below it.

A line of best fit can be used to make predictions.

Example

Amy was away for the maths test. If she got 78% in history, estimate what she would have obtained for maths.

Go to 78% on history scale. Read across to the line, then down. The estimate is approximately 44% in maths.

Averages and range

There are three types of averages: mean, median and mode.

Mean $= \dfrac{\text{Sum of a set of values}}{\text{The number of values used}}$

Median – The middle value when the numbers are put in order of size.

Mode – The one that occurs the most often.

Range – This tells us the spread of information.

Range = highest value – lowest value.

Example

Find the mean, median, mode and range of: 2, 9, 3, 6, 4, 4, 5, 8, 4.

$$\text{Mean} = \frac{2+9+3+6+4+4+5+8+4}{9} = \frac{45}{9} = 5$$

Median 2, 3, 4, 4, 4, 5, 6, 8, 9 Put in order of size.

~~2~~, ~~3~~, ~~4~~, ~~4~~, (4), ~~5~~, ~~6~~, ~~8~~, ~~9~~ Cross off from the end to find the middle.

Median = 4

If there are two numbers in the middle the median is halfway between them.

Mode = 4 as it occurs 3 times.

Range = 9 − 2 = 7

Remember to subtract the two values in order to obtain the range.

Finding averages from a frequency table

A frequency table just tells us **how many** are in a group.

Example

Number of sisters (x)	0	1	2	3	4	5
Frequency (f)	4	9	3	5	2	0

this means that 2 people had 4 sisters

Mean

$$\bar{x} = \frac{\sum fx}{\sum f} = \frac{\text{total of results when multiplied}}{\text{total of frequency}}$$

$$= \frac{(4 \times 0) + (9 \times 1) + (3 \times 2) + (5 \times 3) + (2 \times 4) + (0 \times 5)}{4 + 9 + 3 + 5 + 2 + 0}$$

$$= \frac{38}{23} = 1.65 \text{ (2 d.p.)}$$

Σ means 'the sum of'.

You must remember to divide by the **sum of the frequency**.

Median

Add up the frequencies: 4 + 9 + 3 + 5 + 2 = 23

The median will be the 12th person ______ 12 ______

11 people 11 people

4 + 9 = 13 people so the 12th person has 1 sister. Median = 1.

Mode

This is the one with the highest frequency, that is 1 sister.

For the mode, remember to write down the answer 1, not the number 9 (this is the frequency).

Range

5 − 0 = 5 sisters